LAMBETH STONEWARE

The Woolley Collection
including Doulton Ware
and products of other
British Potteries

by
Rhoda Edwards

London Borough of Lambeth
1973

© London Borough of Lambeth 1973
Published by the London Borough of Lambeth,
14 Knights Hill, London SE27 OHY
Designed by Adrian Hodgkins
Printed by Lund Humphries
ISBN 0/9501893/5/9

The collection includes pottery from Lambeth and other factories, and is at present housed in the Archives and Local History Department of Lambeth Public Libraries, at Minet Library, Knatchbull Road, London SE5 9QY. The majority of the pieces of stoneware catalogued were presented to the Borough of Lambeth in April 1915, by Alderman Charles Woolley, then a member of the Libraries Committee. This collection consists of 208 pieces, of which sixty-four are known to have been made in Lambeth. There are fifty-four marked Doulton pieces. Other Lambeth potters represented are James Stiff, Stephen Green and Thomas Smith. Alderman Woolley initially offered eighty to ninety pieces of pottery, but finally decided to present his entire collection of over 200 items to Lambeth, and not, as originally planned, to the London, Victoria and Albert, and Guildhall Museums. As Alderman Woolley himself said, 'It would be difficult ever to get together again such a powerful and representative collection, even if it were possible. I believe it to be unique, and in many respects I know it to be so.'

The Woolley donation of 1915 included a large number of prints and photographs of topographical interest, which are now part of the Borough Archive and Local History Collection. A catalogue was issued by the Council in May 1915 of both this material and the pottery. The section on the pottery is now enlarged and replaced by the catalogue presented here.

Stoneware and terracotta only have been included, but the Woolley donation also included several pieces of tin-glazed earthenware or delftware, none of which can be ascribed with any certainty to Lambeth.

In addition to the Woolley Collection, Miss Caroline Wright presented several pieces of pottery in 1933 and 1935.

Other ceramics in the Borough's possession include fourteen terracotta plaques by George Tinworth, a leading Doulton artist 1866–1913, which previously belonged to Sir Henry Doulton.

The collection may be viewed by appointment with the Archivist at Minet Library, tel. 01–733–3279.

The author is principally indebted to Miss Dorothy M. Griffiths (of the Department of Ceramics, Victoria and Albert Museum, now of the Department of Artifact Research, National Parks Service, Canada), who kindly examined all the pottery in the collection and suggested amendments to and standardized the form of the catalogue.

Thanks are due to Miss M. Y. Williams, Borough Archivist of the London Borough of Lambeth, for help and encouragement, to the Archives Assistant, Mrs Ruth Schmidt, for assistance in compiling the catalogue, to Michael Hailstone for producing photographs and to Adrian Hodgkins for designing the catalogue.

Alderman Charles Woolley, the donor

Mr Woolley was a distinguished member of Lambeth Borough Council, 1900–12, and was elected Alderman in 1906. He was chairman of several Council committees and a churchwarden at St Mary Lambeth. He was also a prominent citizen of London and member of the Turners' Company. He lived in Dulwich Road, Herne Hill. His antiquarian interests led to him being described as 'The Historian of Lambeth'. He was particularly interested in the pottery manufacture of Lambeth, both historically and for its part in contemporary industry.

His main objective in presenting the pottery collection to the Borough was to provide a nucleus for a Borough Museum. One projected idea after his death in 1922 appears to have been to adapt Brockwell Hall for this purpose. At that date it was hoped: 'that the LCC will accede to the Borough Council's representations so that a museum worthy of the ancient history of the borough may be established. In this way Mr Woolley's signal services to the borough he loved so well will be perpetuated.'

Material relating to the firm of Doulton

The Presentation Volumes

These were presented, with an address to Henry Doulton, by the lady artists in his employment on 26 April 1882. John Sparkes, the Principal of the Lambeth School of Art, acted as chairman at the ceremony. The programme consisted of opening remarks and the presentation of the address by John Sparkes, and a reply by Henry Doulton, with entertainment by the artists upon piano, flute and violin.

The presentation was of two volumes, each 35 × 26 cm, with tooled calf bindings and gilt clasps. Each page is illuminated in colour.

Volume I contains the signatures and marks of all the 'Lady Artists and Assistants' of the Lambeth Art Pottery. Appendices include a list of male artists and assistants; an enumeration of the increase in numbers of lady artists 1871–81; a list of awards obtained for Lambeth Art Pottery; and a list of distinguished persons who had visited the studios and showrooms. This volume is reproduced in full on pages 25–48. Volume II consists of photographs of the lady artists and assistants.

The volumes were purchased by the Borough at the time of the closure of the Doulton Lambeth works in 1956.

Deeds

In 1971, a miscellaneous collection of property deeds, photographs, watercolours, drawings and pamphlets, was presented to the Archives Department by Royal Doulton at the time of their move from Doulton House on the Albert Embankment, which marked the end of the firm's association with Lambeth.

The collection of 162 deeds, of a date range 1770–1899, consists of title deeds to various properties acquired by Doulton's during the expansion of the Lambeth factories. The collection is by no means complete, as the deeds of some of the Lambeth properties have not survived.

None of the deeds refers to the earliest period of the firm's history, when John Doulton had a small pottery at Vauxhall Walk, 1815–26. They all relate to the phases of development of the factory in Lambeth High Street and Fore Street. The terracotta factory on the Albert Embankment south of Broad Street (now Black Prince Road) is not included.

These documents are especially valuable because in almost every instance, at the transfer of ownership to Doulton's, a plan of the property in question was drawn on the deed. These plans also show the layout and ownership of part of the most notorious slum properties in Lambeth, before they were obliterated by the construction of the Albert Embankment or by the new Doulton's buildings.

The High Street Factory

In 1812 John Doulton came to work as a thrower at a small pottery in Vauxhall Walk, Lambeth, after serving a seven-year apprenticeship at the Fulham Pottery. He had thus moved from the oldest established stoneware pottery in London to another area associated for 300 years with pottery making.

Martha Jones, John Doulton's employer, was a widow who had continued to run her husband's business after his death. The Joneses had taken the pottery over from the previous owner, Charles Machall, some time between May 1805 and April 1806, when the entry '– Jones for pottery' first appeared in the parish rate books, assessed on a value of £20. In January 1817, Martha Jones's property had a rateable value of £30.

In June 1815, Martha Jones had taken John Doulton, and her pottery foreman, John Watts, into partnership. This was dissolved in 1820, when Martha retired, and Doulton and Watts formed a new partnership. They were both good businessmen and potters, and by 1826 they had prospered enough to be seeking larger premises.

A suitable pottery was available in Lambeth High Street, one of several crowded into that narrow street. The premises were presumably assigned by the lessee, Henry Willatts of Whitechapel, to Doulton and Watts in 1826. Willatts had obtained the lease from John Ponton in April 1824 (deed 9877). The small plan in the margin of this lease shows the buildings, which consisted of a dwelling house, behind which were a yard and garden, with a kiln-house, warehouse, and stable. The single kiln is shown.

Having obtained this potentially useful site, Doulton and Watts were in no hurry to abandon the Vauxhall Walk pottery. It was kept on until 1829, when John Watts was still paying the rates, but by January 1830, the next door potter, Charles Bloodworth had become the ratepayer.

As the partners had realized, there was room for expansion at Lambeth High Street. Adjoining the pottery on the south was the Jolly Potter public house, which was demolished in 1843, and the site acquired by Doulton (deed 9880). In 1854 a large site was leased, which extended the factory down Lambeth High Street as far as the corner of Broad Street (deed 9882–3). The freehold of this property was bought in 1862 (deed 9887).

The Drainpipe Factory

An important development of the firm was the establishment in December 1846 of a factory solely for the manufacture of drain-pipes. This was prompted by the demand for urban sanitary reform at this period. The factory was begun by the lease of a small pottery and adjoining buildings on the opposite side of Lambeth High Street to the main factory (deed 9916).

Yet another small pottery was added to the drainpipe factory in 1854 (deed 9948). This was situated in Fore Street and had belonged to Richard Waters, then to Alexander Boughton and William Garraway.

The drainpipe factory also expanded north into Ferry Street (deed 9969), and gradually covered the whole area between High Street and Fore Street, terminating on the north side of James Stiff's pottery:

deeds 9977 (1857), 9978–9 (1863), 9989 (1865), 9992 (1864), 9999 (1871), 10,008 (1874), 10,009–10 (1877), 10,019 (1882), 10, 027 (1893), 10,032 (1895).

Although only one deed referring to it exists, it is clear that some time between 1852 and 1874, a pottery in Ferry Street belonging to William Batstone was leased by Doulton's. Janeway's pottery, also in Ferry Street, was bought in 1880.

The Albert Embankment Docks

The old ramshackle loading stages overhanging the Thames were swept away in 1861 during the construction of the Albert Embankment and replaced by docks under the embankment itself. Arrangements were made with the Metropolitan Board of Works for the building of the docks, and with Doulton's neighbour, James Stiff (deeds 10,000–07).

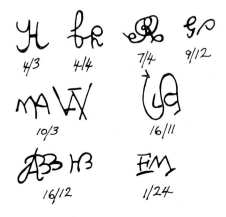

Catalogue of Stoneware Pottery, including the Woolley Collection and Terracotta Plaques by George Tinworth

Abbreviations

H=height/L=length/BD=base diameter/D=diameter/RD=rim diameter/PV=presentation volume

Doulton stamps are referred to by the numbers assigned to them in Desmond Eyles, *Royal Doulton 1815–1965* (London, 1965) Appendix II, pages 191–6.

The pieces are numbered in accordance with the system of storage, i.e. 2/1 is shelf 2, item 1.

Mugs

2/1   Buff, top half brown. Stamped with printer's type on side, 'Francis Smith Billericay 1794'. Handle restored. Excise stamp on side by handle, WR and crown. H 13 cm; BD 9 cm.

2/2   Dark buff, brown rim band. Letter 'C' stamped on side, under acid-etched mark 'Pint GR 189'. H 13·5 cm; BD 8·5 cm.

2/3   Olive and buff solid agate fabric. Stamped floral motif round centre and on handle. Bands of imitation rope whipping to resemble a wooden bucket. Silver rim. Mark, Eyles no.11 and 'England 7190 nn'. H 13 cm; BD 12·5 cm.

2/4   Dark buff, brown rim. Applied flower motif round rim. Applied heads of Queen Victoria, young and old. Inscription with decorative line in white trailed slip, 'Victoria R.I.' and '1837–1897'. Mark, Eyles no.4 and 7507. H 9·5 cm; BD 7·5 cm.

2/5   Buff, brown rim. Applied hunting scene of the kill. Moulded greyhound handle. H 10·5 cm; BD 10 cm.

2/6   Dark buff, brown rim band. Applied toby and hunting scenes. 'ONE PINT' stamped on side. Mark 'T.SMITH & CO. OLD KENT RD. LONDON'. H 10·5 cm; BD 10 cm.

2/7   Dark buff, brown rim. Applied hunting scenes. 'One pint' stamped on side. Mark 'T.SMITH & Co. OLD KENT RD·'. H 10·5 cm; BD 10 cm.

2/8–   Buff, darker rim bands. Applied toby, hunting,
2/13   windmill scenes. H 10·5 cm; BD 9·5 cm. Set of six.

2/14–   Buff, darker rim band. Applied toby, hunting,
2/15   windmill scenes. H 13·5 cm; BD 12 cm. Pair.

13/8   Grey. Narrow reeded neck. Incised elaborate floral motifs with blue glaze. Purple wash on neck. H 14 cm; BD 6 cm.

13/9   Grey. Narrow reeded neck. Incised simple floral motifs with blue glaze. Applied small medallion, stamped 'GR'. Purple wash on neck. H 15·5 cm; BD 6 cm.

1/14   Buff. Tall, very narrow cylindrical mug. Ridged handle. H 14·5 cm; BD 4·5 cm.

Goblets

3/1   Dark buff, brown rim band. Applied toby and hunting scenes. H 15 cm; BD 9 cm.

3/2   Buff, brown rim band. Applied toby on body and hunting scenes round foot. H 13 cm; BD 8·5 cm.

3/3   Buff, brown rim band. Applied hunting scenes. H 13 cm; BD 9 cm.

Beakers

3/4–   Buff, brown rim band. Applied toby, hunting
3/5   scenes, tree and windmill. Silver rim. H 11 cm; BD 7 cm. A pair.

3/6   Buff, brown rim band. Applied toby, trees, flowers, windmill. Stamped on side 'H. WRIGHT'. H 9 cm; BD 5·5 cm.

3/7   Buff, olive green majolica glaze on rim band. White applied toby and hunting scenes. Mark, Eyles no.4 and 3768. H 12 cm; BD 5 cm.

3/8   Buff, brown rim band. Dark brown inscription, 'Vessels large may venture more But little boats should keep near shore'. Mark, Eyles no.4 and 5418. H 12 cm; BD 5·5 cm.

3/9–   Dark buff, brown rim band. White applied
3/10   medallion, 'National Rifle Association. founded 1860'. Date 1860–89 and 'Wimbledon' in stamp-applied letters. Mark, Eyles no.6 and 846 and PV 159. H 11 cm; BD 5·5 cm. A pair.

Loving Cups

3/11   Double salt-glaze. Cream, brown rim band. Applied scenes of monkeys in drapery and feathers, drinking and smoking. Two handles. Mark 'Powell Bristol' incorporated in decoration on wine bottles and jug. H 13 cm; BD 11·5 cm.

3/12   Buff, brown rim band. Applied royal arms and a hare and pheasant among foliage. Three moulded greyhound handles. H 16 cm; BD 16 cm.

4/1 Buff. Incised pony heads in blue, rouletted decoration round rim. Three handles, majolica glazed in brown and blue. Mark, Eyles no.6 (1874) and 440 and PV 93. H 16 cm; BD 13·5 cm.

4/2 Cream. Incised ducks chased by cat, in blue. Incised lines and rouletted Greek key pattern. One handle. Mark, Eyles no.5. H 16·5 cm; BD 14·5 cm.

4/3 Grey/green, blue and buff majolica glazes. White slip inscription 'Born 1758 died 1805', in commemoration of Lord Nelson. Three handles in imitation of ropes. Mark, Eyles no.23 and 4039 also see p.8. H 16·5 cm; BD 16·5 cm.

4/4 Brown, dark blue, mottled blue and green majolica glazes. Bell shaped. Applied moulded flower motifs and inscription, 'The Council of the Borough of Lambeth Tug of War 11th July 1903'. Three handles, one riveted. Mark, Eyles no.23 and 2299 nn also see p.8. H 17·5 cm; BD 10·5 cm.

4/5 Buff. Incised symmetrical motifs of flowers and leaves in blue and brown majolica glazes. Two handles. Silver rim. Mark, Eyles no.5. H 16 cm; BD 13 cm.

4/6 Buff, brown rim band. Applied white toby, hunting scenes. Inscription: 'T. South South Church 1890' in white stamp—applied slip. Three moulded greyhound handles. Mark, Eyles no.11 and 2951 and PV 159. H 17·5 cm; BD 14·5 cm.

4/7 Buff. Impressed overall small floral motif with white applied horse-racing scenes. Three handles decorated in blue and olive stripes in majolica glazes. Mark, Eyles no.11 and 1882 and PV 188. H 16·5 cm; BD 12·5 cm.

Jugs

5/1 Buff, brown rim and shoulders. Applied toby, hunting scenes, windmill and St George and Dragon. Handle terminal grapes and vine leaf. H 21 cm; BD 13 cm.

5/2 Buff, brown rim and shoulders. Applied toby, hunting scenes, windmill and tree. Handle terminal vine leaves, grapes, and rivet. H 22 cm; BD 10 cm.

5/3 Buff, dark brown rim and shoulders. Applied hunting scenes, toby, trees. Handle terminal a foliate motif and rivet. H 25 cm; BD 13·5 cm.

5/4 Buff, light brown rim and shoulders. Applied toby, hunting scenes, windmill, tree, horse and groom medallion. H 19 cm; BD 14 cm.

5/5 Buff, brown rim and shoulders. Applied toby, hunting scenes. Handle terminal vine leaves, grapes and rivet. H 23 cm; BD 13 cm.

5/6 Dark buff, brown rim and shoulders. Applied hunting scenes, windmill, trees and hare coursing. Handle terminal foliate motif and rivet. Mark stamped on base, 'FULHAM POTTERY & CO. FULHAM LONDON S.W.'. H 21 cm; BD 11 cm.

5/7 Buff, brown rim and shoulders. Applied toby, hunting scenes, tree and windmill. Handle terminal vine leaves and rivet. H 19 cm; BD 10·5 cm.

5/8 Buff, brown handle, rim and shoulders. Moulded greyhound handle. Applied vine motif round neck. Applied hunting scenes of kills of boar and stag. Pouring lip restored. 'T' incised on base. H 17·5 cm; BD 10 cm.

6/1 Dark buff, brown rim and shoulders. Applied toby, hunting scenes, windmill with house, and donkey with sack on back. Handle terminal foliate motif and rivet. 'A' stamped on base. H 24 cm; BD 13 cm.

6/2 Buff, brown rim and shoulders. Applied toby, drinking and hunting scenes. Handle terminal bunch of small leaves and rivet. H 25 cm; BD 12·5 cm.

6/3 Brown glazed earthenware in imitation of stoneware. Applied nymphs, satyr's masks, flowers, windmills, lions, grapes, toby, tree and a crown. Thick smear of brown and yellow glaze on base in an attempt to seal a crack. H 29 cm; BD 14·5 cm.

6/4 White. Interior only glazed. Moulded overall with dead game hanging heads down. Moulded greyhound handle. Rim edge irregularly fluted. Foot fluted at edge. Small 6 or 9 stamped on base. H 26·5 cm; BD 14·5 cm.

6/5 Cream. White lead glaze inside. Applied hunting scenes of boar and stag at kill. Vine motif round neck and crenellated pattern on shoulder. Moulded greyhound handle. Stamped 'G' and 'M' on base. H 20 cm; BD 12·5 cm.

6/6 Dark buff, brown top. Ovoid form with wide spout on one side and narrow on the other. Narrow has metal mount, wide a cork and metal stopper. Applied coat of arms of Salisbury or New Sarum (see Eyles pp.79–80 for Old Sarum Kettle). Base stamped 'The orignal Salisbury Kettle Charles Haskins Poultry Cross Salisbury'. H 30 cm; BD 10·5 cm.

7/1 Buff, brown upper half. Moulded coat of arms, Victoria and Albert heads and harvest motifs. Marked with the wreath from the Stephen Green, Lambeth mark, but with the name missing. H 12 cm; BD 8 cm.

7/2 Buff, brown rim and shoulders. Moulded 'Silenus' form. H 14·5 cm; BD 7·5 cm.

7/3 Green stoneware. Moulded 'Silenus' form. Mark 'No.19' enclosed in wreath and scroll. Impressed 30 (probably Minton's). H 13·5 cm; BD 8 cm.

7/4 Buff, brown rim. Moulded in head of a satyr. Mark incised on base, see p.8. H 10 cm; BD 6 cm.

7/5 Cream, buff top. 'Silenus' form, with very blurred moulding. H 16 cm; BD 10·5 cm.

7/6 Buff, brown rim and shoulders. Moulded 'Silenus' form. H 19 cm; BD 11 cm.

7/7 Buff, brown rim. Moulded 'Silenus' form. H 20·5 cm; BD 13 cm.

7/8 Buff, brown head and shoulders. Moulded in the form of Toby Filpot seated on a barrel, holding a foaming pot. Coat textured with impressed sacking. Handle formed by the queue of his wig. Mark, Eyles no.4 and 304 and S oo and PV 204. H 22 cm; BD 9 cm.

7/9 Buff, brown rim. Moulded in form of standing Toby Filpot looking at his watch. H 21 cm; BD 11 cm.

7/10 Buff. Moulded in form of a monkey in squatting attitude in a monk's habit. Lid formed by top of monkey's head with loop for chain to attach it to his cowl. Spout formed by tail. Probably a coffee pot. H 22 cm; BD 10·5 cm.

7/11 Buff, brown horizontal bands. Puzzle jug. Stamped and applied floral motifs in brown and buff. H 15·5 cm; BD 6·5 cm.

7/12 Buff. Moulded in form of head of the Duke of Wellington. Handle decorated with military accoutrements. Mark 'Stephen Green Lambeth' within a wreath, on base. H 15 cm; BD 9 cm.

7/13 Buff. Moulded bust of Lord Nelson, his hat forming the rim. Handle missing. Mark, Eyles no. 23 and 'Replica of the original jug made by Doulton & Watts Lambeth' stamped on base. H 19 cm; B 11·5 × 11 cm.

8/1 Buff, brown neck and shoulders. Applied floral sprays and Phoebus in chariot. H 8 cm; BD 4·5 cm.

8/2 Buff, dark brown neck and shoulders. Applied toby, windmill and tree motifs. H 9·5 cm; BD 6 cm.

8/3 Buff, brown neck and shoulders. Applied toby, hunting scenes, trees and flowers. Handle terminal foliate motif and rivet. H 13 cm; BD 8 cm.

8/4 Buff, darker neck and shoulders. Applied toby, hunting scenes, trees, windmill with house. Handle terminal foliate motif and rivet. H 14 cm; BD 7 cm.

8/5 Buff, brown neck and shoulders. Applied toby, stag hunting, windmill with house and tree motifs. Handle terminal foliate motif and rivet. H 13 cm; BD 8 cm.

8/6 Buff, darker neck and shoulders. Ovoid shape. Applied hunting scenes, tree and dancing boy. Acanthus leaves round base, leaves and flowers round neck. H 14 cm; BD 7 cm.

8/7 Buff, brown neck and shoulders. Applied toby, hunting scenes, trees. Handle terminal a bunch of leaves and rivet. H 14 cm; BD 7 cm.

8/8 Buff, brown neck and shoulders. Applied toby, hunting scenes, windmill, tree and flower motifs. Handle terminal foliate motif and rivet. Circular stamp on base 'Hot Water Proof'. H 15 cm; BD 9 cm.

8/9 Buff, brown neck and shoulders. Applied toby, hunting scenes, trees. Handle terminal bunch of leaves and rivet. H 14 cm; BD 8 cm.

8/10 Buff, brown neck and shoulders. Applied toby, trees, hounds, windmill. Reeded neck. Handle terminal foliate motif and rivet. H 14 cm; BD 8 cm.

8/11 Buff, light brown neck and shoulders. Applied toby, hunting scenes, and windmill. Handle terminal foliate motif and rivet. H 16 cm; BD 8·5 cm

8/12 Cream, blue neck and shoulders. Applied toby, hunting scenes, tree, windmill with house. Handle terminal foliate motif and rivet. H 17 cm; BD 9·5 cm.

8/13 Buff, brown rim and shoulders. Applied toby, hunting scenes, trees. Handle terminal a bunch of small leaves and rivet. Silver lid. H 22 cm including lid; BD 9 cm.

9/1 Earthenware in imitation of stoneware. Buff, brown neck, shoulders, and handle. Moulded in form of thatched cottage with ivy. H 11 cm; BD 7·5 cm.

9/2 Buff, brown neck and shoulders. Handle terminal in form of a leaf and rivet. Mark 'J. Stiff & Sons London'. H 10·5 cm; BD 6 cm.

9/3 Dark brown. Two incised horizontal lines. H 13 cm; BD 8 cm.

9/4 Dark buff, brown neck and shoulders. Handle terminal in form of a leaf and rivet. Mark 'J. Stiff & Sons London'. H 14 cm; BD 8·5 cm.

9/5 Buff, brown neck, shoulders and handle. Narrow neck. Applied female head on neck and base of handle. Mark, Eyles no.5. H 17·5 cm; BD 7 cm.

9/6 Buff, brown neck, shoulders and handle. Narrow neck. Applied female head on neck and base of handle. H 19·5 cm; BD 7 cm.

9/7 Buff, brown band top and bottom with narrow moulded bands in form of a barrel. Transfer print in brown of two oval portraits of Queen Victoria 1837 and 1897, with the words, 'She wrought her people lasting good', also a crest and words 'Dei Gratia Victoria Queen & Empress' above it. Mark, Eyles no.4. H 18·5 cm; BD 9 cm.

9/8 Buff, brown neck. Wide necked. Applied vine leaves and cherubs. Satyr under pouring lip. Stamp-applied inscription in olive green, 'Good is not enough the best is not too good', around side. Mark, Eyles no.11 and 184 and 306, assistant's mark blurred. H 18 cm; BD 9 cm; RD 13 cm.

9/9 Buff, brown rim. Applied white medallions of young and old Queen Victoria, with inscription, '1837–1897 Long to reign over us God save the Queen' and 'A.C.C.', in white stamp-applied clay. Mark, Eyles no.4 and 4763 and PV 182. H 18·5 cm; BD 9·5 cm.

9/10 Buff, decorated in blue, grey, grey/green, and brown majolica glazes. Stamped small motifs and overall jewelling. Handle in form of a sea monster. Mark incised on base, 'A16 RW Martin London 12–1874'. H 15 cm; BD 9·5 cm.

9/11 Dark buff. Narrow neck. Entirely covered with horizontal rouletting. Mark, Eyles no.5. H 21 cm; BD 7 cm.

9/12 Dark buff, brown neck and shoulders. Narrow neck. Floral transfer print in brown. Mark, Eyles no.4 and 9320 also GP see p.8. H 12 cm; BD 4·5 cm.

9/13 Brown neck and base with wide buff band extending from shoulder. Narrow neck. Floral transfer print in brown. Mark, Eyles no.4 and 9319. H 14·5 cm; BD 4 cm.

9/14 Buff, dark brown neck and rim. Narrow neck. Floral transfer print in brown. Mark, Eyles no.4 and 9884. H 21 cm; BD 9 cm.

10/1 Brown, pale buff pouring lip and base. Applied buff leaf and flower garland motif. Pale buff rolled and twisted handle. H 19 cm; BD 8 cm.

10/2 Dark Brown. Rouletted band round shoulder. H 19 cm; BD 10·5 cm.

10/3 Buff, narrow moulded bands in brown. Applied moulded medallion of Disraeli, surmounted by an earl's coronet. Impressed inscription, 'Benjamin Disraeli Earl of Beaconsfield, Born Dec. 21, 1804. Died April 19, 1881. I will sit down now, but the time will come when you will hear me. House of Commons, 7 Dec. 1837', and 'I have begun several things many times and I have often succeeded at last', round body and neck. Mark, Eyles no.6. Registration mark and 'John MORTLOCK OXFORD STREET LONDON' in an oval. Also see p.8. H 22 cm; BD 10 cm.

10/4 Dark buff, upper half dark brown. Ovoid shape. Reeded neck. Handle with thumbed end. H 20 cm; BD 10·5 cm.

10/5 Buff, brown neck. Transfer printed in black with heads of Lord Roberts, Baden-Powell and Bryan Mahon, with colonial emblems and 'South Africa 1900' in a ribbon. Mark, Eyles no.4 and 4724. H 21 cm; BD 11 cm.

10/6 Dark buff, narrow relief bands of brown at base, middle of body, and rim. Moulded bearded mask under pouring lip. Stamp-applied inscription between centre bands, 'The more the merrier the fewer the better cheer'. Applied dark green acanthus leaves at base of body. Mark, Eyles no.11 and PV 112, 153, 157. H 21·5 cm; BD 9·5 cm.

10/7 Light brown. Moulded in imitation of leather jug. Impressed on side, 'Model of the Ancient Leather Jack of St. Cross, Winchester 1405'. Mark TM in interwoven Gothic capitals and monogram JC Old Quay Runcorn (John Cliff, previously at Lambeth). H 20·5 cm; BD 12·5 cm.

10/8 Brown. Narrow neck. Applied vine leaves and angler. Mark semi-obliterated, . . . PRES . . . ALLOA, also an oval incised within another. H 24·5 cm; BD 8·5 cm.

18/3 Grey. Blue horizontal bands with vertical stripes enclosing a floral motif. Mark at base of handle '$\frac{1}{2}$'. H 34 cm; BD 12 cm.

Tea Pot

13/1 Buff, brown rim, shoulders and lid. Globular shape. White applied toby, hunting scenes, windmill and tree. Buff garland on lid. Flower and leaf terminal on handle. Mark, Eyles no.4 and 1632 and PV 69. H 15 cm including lid; BD 9 cm.

Bottles

13/2 Buff. Applied holly leaves in dark blue and brown majolica glazes. 'WHISKY' stamped on raised label on shoulder. Blue squared handle. Metal and cork stopper. Registration mark on handle. H 21·5 cm; BD 8·5 cm.

13/3 Bellarmine type. Speckled brown glaze, no decoration. Restored handle. H 21 cm; BD 6 cm.

13/4 Bellarmine type. Face mask and medallion of double-headed eagle and crown. H 21 cm; BD 5·5 cm.

13/5 Bellarmine type. Tall cylindrical neck. Pale grey and brown speckled glaze. Base restored. H 21·5 cm.

13/6 Bellarmine type. Face mask and three heraldic medallions, splashed with blue. Handle restored. Whorled base. H 22 cm; BD 11·5 cm.

13/7   Dark buff, brown neck, shoulders and handle. Narrow neck. Mark, Eyles no.5. H 20·5 cm; BD 6 cm.

18/1   Brown and buff. Moulded in the form of a fat man, in night-cap with spout on end. H 29 cm; BD 23 cm.

18/2   Buff, darker rim and shoulders. Narrow neck for cork. Probably had wicker jacket. Mark, Eyles no.4 stamped on side. H 30 cm; BD 14 cm.

Flasks

14/1   Buff, brown wash on upper half. Moulded fish. L 17 cm.

14/2   As 14/1. L 21 cm.

14/3   Brown. Flat sided. Moulded medallion within a circle, of an exotic bird on nest. Reverse plain, with circle. D 8·5 cm.

14/4   Brown. Moulded in shape of a shot flask with fluted design and hounds. Impressed with printer's type, 'Mr James Hutchens Baker & Basket'. (1842 Kelly's Directory has – James Hutchens, 'Baker & Basket', 12 Red Lion Street, Whitechapel). Neck broken. H 16 cm.

14/5   Buff, brown neck. Moulded in shape similar to 14/4. Stamped on edge at base, 'Stephen Green Imperial Potteries Lambeth'. H 24 cm.

14/6   Buff. Moulded in form of a clock and stamped 'Railway chronometer'. Mark, 'Smith Lambeth' stamped on base. H 18 cm.

14/7   Buff, brown neck and shoulders. Moulded heads either side of Napoleon and Dante, with names impressed beneath each. H 15 cm.

14/8   Buff. 'Indian club' shape. 'STOCKER'S EFFERVESCING GINGER BEER. UNFERMENTED', stamped on side, and 'ROYAL AERATED WATERWORKS, 13 THOMAS ST. STAMFORD ST. BLACKFRIARS' on other side. L 21 cm.

14/9   Buff, brown hat. Moulded sailor astride an upright rum barrel. H 21 cm.

14/10   Buff, dark brown upper half. Moulded in form of Lord Brougham, holding in his hands a scroll with the words impressed, 'The True Spirit of REFORM', and under it, 'BROUGHAM REFORM CORDIAL'. Mark stamped on back, 'Lambeth Pottery Doulton & Watts 15 High St.'. H 17·5 cm.

14/11   Buff. Moulded in form of an old woman, cloaked and bonneted, with a bottle in her hand. H 19 cm.

14/12   Buff, upper part brown. Moulded with figures of Punch and dog on one side, and prancing imp and Punch on a donkey on the other side. On side one, Punch holds up a scroll with the words, 'THE TRIUMPH OF THE PEN'. Stamped on base, 'DOULTON WATTS LAMBETH POTTERY London'. H 18 cm.

14/13   Pale buff. Moulded in the shape of a barrel bound with bands. Applied label on top impressed with 'Sinclair Mile End Gate'. H 10 cm.

14/14   Buff. Moulded in shape of a barrel bound with bands. Label on top impressed with 'S Green Lambeth'. H 13 cm.

14/15   As 14/14 with 'S Green Potter Lambeth' on label. H 13 cm

14/16   Buff. Moulded in form of flap fastening book. 'Blucks Railway Companion' impressed in printer's type on spine. H 11 cm.

14/17   Buff. Moulded in form of flap fastening book. H 15 cm.

14/18–   Pale buff double salt-glaze, darker neck and
14/20   shoulders. Fluted moulding on shoulders. Stamped on base, 'J. STIFF LONDON POTTERY LAMBETH'. H 15 cm. Set of three.

14/21   As 14/18–20 in buff ordinary salt-glaze ware. H 15 cm.

Tobacco Jars

15/1   Buff, brown rim. Applied toby, tree, nymphs. Lid missing. H 7·5 cm; BD 8·5 cm.

15/2   Buff, brown rim. Applied drinking scenes. Rouletted beading top and bottom. Lid missing. H 9 cm; BD 10 cm.

15/3   Buff double salt-glaze, darker rim band and lid. Applied drinking scenes on sides and flowers on lid. Rouletted bands top and bottom. H 15·5 cm; BD 11·5 cm.

15/4   Buff. Rectangular with domed lid. Applied 'Tom, Tom, the piper's son' scene on one side and toby scene on the other, also plant motifs. Very small leaf lug handles. H 13 cm; BD 11 × 8 cm.

15/5   Buff, upper part darker. Moulded figures of saints. H 9 cm; BD 7·5 cm.

15/6   Brown, lower half dark buff. Moulded figures of saints. Octagonal lid. H 18·5 cm; BD 10 cm.

15/7   Dark buff, brown lid. Moulded in shape of a barrel. Lid has a man's head with nightcap as handle. Pipe and smoking accessories on lid. 'G.M.C.DONALD' stamped on side. Mark 'H H' stamped on base. H 13 cm; BD 7 cm.

15/8 Buff, brown bands. Moulded in form of a barrel bound with metal. Lid has a man's head with a nightcap as handle. Pipe and smoking accessories on lid. Mark on inside of lid, '1882 H H'. H 15 cm; BD 8·5 cm.

15/9 Buff, dark brown bands. Moulded in form of a barrel. Applied white floral and stamped circle motifs. Applied brown medallion with head of Disraeli in white. Lid has brown acanthus leaves and blue/green flowers. Mark, Eyles no.11 and PV 55, 172, 179. H 13·5 cm; BD 8·5 cm.

15/10 Buff with brown, grey/green majolica glazes. Brown marbled lid. Trailed slip inscription. 'William Ewart Gladstone' and 'Effort Honest, manful humble effort Succeeds by its reflective action upon character better than success'. Applied medallion head of W. E. Gladstone. Mark, Eyles no.4 and England 8467 and PV 204. H 13 cm; BD 8 cm.

15/11 Buff, overfired blue majolica glaze. Heavy applied ivy trail motif overall. Lid surmounted by figure of a man seated on a stool, to serve as a handle. Stamped motif round lid edge. Mark 'Frank Barratt' incised on footring and FB monogram on stool on lid. H 19 cm; BD 14·5 cm.

Jars

15/12 Buff body, dark brown glaze. Moulded in shape of an urn on square base, with lid. Face masks under two lug handles. Knob on lid restored. H 20·5 cm; BD 10 cm.

15/13– Blue/grey fabric, blue glaze. Applied figures of
15/14 dancing boys and jewelling in white. Stamped flower motif round shoulder. Lid plain, flat with recessed knob. Mark, Eyles no. 11 and 1881 and PV 172. H 8 cm; BD 5 cm. A pair.

16/1 Brown leopard-skin glaze, bottom third buff. H 12·5 cm; BD 6·5 cm.

15/15 Lid of jar. Dark buff, brown band within incised circles, brown knob. Applied light buff cherubs blowing trumpets. Riveted. Mark PV 181. H 3·5 cm; D 9·5 cm.

Bowls

16/2 Buff fabric, with majolica glazes in blue, blue/green, green, and brown. Incised leaf motifs round base. Panels with deeply cut relief ivy leaves on sides. Mark, Eyles no.9 and 1878 and PV 50, 61. H 12·5 cm; BD 9·5 cm.

16/3 Dark buff, brown bands at rim and base, transfer printed floral design in brown. Mark, Eyles no.4 and 2301. H 10·5 cm; BD 6·5 cm.

Vases

16/4 Silicon ware. Buff. Applied white, blue and pale blue/green flower motif in stamp-applied clay. Rouletted bands round body. Mark, Eyles no. 19 and 6124 and 'a e'. H 10 cm; BD 6 cm.

16/5 Silicon ware. Buff. Stamp-applied white orange blossom and fruit motifs. Stamp-applied rouletted blue bands. Mark, Eyles no.19 and 1884 and 'o pd'. H 9 cm; BD 6 cm.

16/6– Silicon ware. Buff. Applied abstract plant
16/7 motif in blue, white, and blue/green. White stamp—applied clay jewelling on shoulder. Mark, Eyles no.23 or 24, without lion or crown, and SILICON 51834. H 10 cm; BD 3 cm. A pair.

16/8– Grey unglazed stoneware. Globular shape.
16/9 Flaring necks. White applied ivy and acanthus leaves and black dots. Mark, Eyles no.11 and 1883 and 8930 and PV 162, 159. H 12 cm; BD 4 cm. A pair.

16/10– Silicon ware. Pale grey/buff. Formal design in
16/11 brown and pale blue slip round neck and base. Incised buff apple branch design on body. Mark, Eyles no.19 and 1884 and 720 II also see p.8. H 26 cm; BD 6 cm. A pair. 16/11 has section missing from rim.

16/12– Buff fabric. Ovoid with long narrow necks.
16/13 Decorated in dark blue, blue/green, brown/green majolica glazes, and in white slip. Lines of white jewelling. Mark, Eyles no.6 and 1876 and PV 52. Also see p.8. H 27 cm; BD 7·5 cm. A pair. Rim of 16/12 chipped.

16/14 Buff. Incised long leaf design in dark blue with rows of jewelling in pale blue along centre of leaves. Mark, Eyles no.6 and 1873 and initials of Frank A. Butler. H 25 cm; BD 8·5 cm.

16/15 Grey. Incised floral sprays filled in with blue overall. Grey/green glaze on edge of foot, brown on rim. Handle has incised pattern coloured blue. Mark, Eyles no.9 and 1877 and PV 8, 110, 180, five *fleur-de-lis* and 'c w'. H 22 cm; BD 9·5 cm.

Flower Pot Holder

18/4 Dark blue, green and brown majolica glazes on pierced design of ivy. Stand octagonal, glazed in blue and brown. Mark, Eyles, no.9 and 1880 and PV 93, 160. H 23 cm; BD 18 cm; RD 18·5 cm.

Funnel

11/1 Dark buff. Inside word 'Condemd' incised. Two small holes for suspension. H 12 cm; RD 9·5 cm.

Water Filters

11/2 Buff. Lid and decoration picked out in brown. Applied royal coat of arms and 'V R'. Rouletted horizontal bands. Lid has restored knob. Accompanying spigot and interior filter plate. H 22 cm; BD 9 cm; RD 11 cm.

11/3 Cream. Applied lion's head on either side and royal arms above label, 'G. CHEAVINS IMPROVED PATENT GOLD MEDAL SELF CLEANING RAPID WATER FILTER BOSTON ENGLAND', all between horizontal ribbed bands. A spigot hole at foot on either side. H 18 cm; BD 11·5 cm.

Hot Water Bottles

11/4   Cream. Round, flat sided, stopper at neck. Black transfer printed on one side, 'THE "ADAPTABLE" HOT WATER BOTTLE AND BED WARMER MADE AT THE OLD FULHAM POTTERY ALL WATER BOTTLES SHOULD BE WARMED BEFORE BEING FILLED WITH BOILING WATER', and 'Reg. no. 443310'. D 18 cm.

11/5   Brown. Hemispherical shape. Moulded Prince of Wales' feathers four times in form of a cross round neck at top. Knob in form of a flower at one end. Stopper missing. B 24·5 × 12·5 cm.

Pie Dish

12/1   Dark brown outside, white slip coating inside. Two small lug handles, four pad feet. H 8·5 cm; L 24·5 cm.

Storage Jars

12/2   Dark brown. Straight sides. Rouletted bands on sides. Flat lid. H 19 cm; BD 11 cm.

12/3   Brown. Straight sides flaring to shoulder. No lid. H 15·5 cm; BD 8 cm.

12/4   Brown. Straight sides, tapered to base. Rouletted band round middle. No lid. H 16 cm; BD 9·5 cm.

12/5   Dark buff, lid and rim dark brown. Globular shape. Band of rouletting round body. Two lug handles. Three steam vents in lid. H 14 cm; BD 10 cm.

12/6   Brown. Straight sides. Rouletted bands round body. Two lug handles. H 17 cm; BD 14 cm.

12/7   Lid in dark brown earthenware, accompanying 12/6 does not belong to it.

12/8   Brown. Ovoid shape. Band of rouletting round shoulder. Two lug handles. Flat lid. H 17·5 cm; BD 10·5 cm.

12/9   Dark brown. Ovoid shape. Rouletted band round body. Two lug handles. Flat lid. H 18 cm; BD 10·5 cm.

Plaques

17/1   Buff. Circular. Carved olive-brown bird on flower stems, stippled background. Recess cut in back with two holes for suspension. D 10·5 cm.

17/2   Terracotta. Circular. Moulded seated nymph and cherub. One hole for suspension. Lacquered front. D 18 cm.

Garden Tile

17/3   Brown. Lower half shaped to sink in the earth. Upper half deeply incised with interlaced ribbons, containing alternate circles and stars, on one side only. H 16·5 cm; W 22·5 cm.

Ink Pots

1/1   Brown. Oval. Moulded in form of a woman's head. Two pen holes. L 8 cm.

1/2   Light brown. Moulded in the form of a lion's head. Two pen holes. L 6 cm.

1/3–   Buff, darker shoulders. Narrow cylindrical
1/4   bodies. H 5·5 cm. A pair.

1/5–   Brown. Round, squared-off shoulders. H 5 cm;
1/7   BD 5·5; 5; 4·5 cm.

Condiment Pots

1/8   Pale buff double salt-glaze, darker rim. Tall ovoid form. Applied motif enclosing letter 'S' as trade mark. Mark 'STIFF LONDON' stamped on base. H 9·5 cm.

1/9   Dark brown. Storage jar form. Mark 'G G' stamped on base. H 9 cm.

1/10   Cream, brown top. Pepper-pot, with hole in base for filling. Applied leaves and hounds. H 7·5 cm.

1/24   Buff fabric. Incised foliage motifs and flowers in blue, brown, white and grey/green majolica glazes, contained in panels on body. Neck threaded for screw top. Mark, Eyles no.11 and 1882 also see p.8 and 205. H 7 cm; BD 4 cm; RD 2 cm.

Spirit Barrel Samples

1/11   Buff, brown top and bottom. Turned bands round bottom and round aperture on top and spigot hole on side at base. Stamped on side 'GIN 1862'. H 9·5 cm.

1/12   As 1/11. Mark 'N N' stamped on base. H 9·5 cm.

Spirit Measure

1/13   Dark brown outside, inner surface lighter. Single incised line round rim. H 6·5 cm; RD 6·5 cm.

Jelly Moulds

1/15   Dark brown. Incised line round outside of rim. Inside moulded in formal design. H 5 cm. L 9·5 cm.

1/16   Dark brown. Inside moulded in corn design. H 5 cm; L 13 cm.

Dishes

1/17   Buff, top edge light brown on outer side. Moulded in form of a basket. Formal design of leaves and flowers on outside. Rim L 12 cm.

1/26   Buff. Light brown wash on one side. Oval shape. Moulded flower sprays on each side. 'Rope twist' piping at rim and base. Two small lug handles moulded as lion's heads at either end. H 5 cm; B 11 × 8 cm.

Money Boxes

1/18   Buff earthenware with dark brown glaze. Moulded in form of head of a fat man wearing a nightcap. Marked with large five-pointed star in slight relief on base. H 9·5 cm.

1/19   As 1/18 in lighter brown, without star mark.

1/20   Dark buff, brown roof. Moulded in form of a cottage. Date 1874 scratched on base. H 10·5 cm; BL 13 cm.

1/21   Cream double salt-glaze, buff roof. Moulded in form of a cottage. 'Savings Bank' in blurred letters stamped over door. H 10·5 cm; BL 13 cm.

11/6   Dark brown. Modelled in form of a wooden chest covered in bark, marked with incised lines. Imitations of staple fastenings and hinges. On base is drawn an armoured knight in incised lines, within an incised frame. B 20·5 × 14·5 cm.

Trap Model

1/22   Light brown. Sample of patent WC trap (used in conjunction with pan). H 4·5 cm.

Jug Sample

1/23   Buff fabric. Incised foliage motifs in blue, white and grey/green majolica glazes. Mark, Eyles no.11 and 1884 and 223, initials of Florence E. Barlow and PV 211. H 7 cm; BD 3·5 cm.

Flower Pot Sample

1/25   Pale buff, brown rim. Moulded flowers round body. Simple everted rim. Hole in centre of base. H 5 cm; BD 3·5 cm; RD 6·5 cm.

Shoes

1/27a– White. Moulded shoes with pale blue laces and
1/27b toe-caps. H 3·5 cm; L 8·5 cm.

Carpenter's Bag

1/28   Buff and brown. Modelled in form of raffia basket on a base, containing a saw, plane and other tools. Mark, Eyles no.9 and 'E A' and Rd 162583. 11·5 × 7·5 cm.

Boy Musicians

1/29   Boy with tambourine. Broken. Mark, Eyles no.11. H 11 cm.

1/30   Boy with horn. Damaged. Mark 'Doultons Lambeth' incised on base. H 12 cm. Both incised with monogram of George Tinworth.

Terracotta Plaques by George Tinworth

All mounted in wooden frames with glass fronts, and inscribed by Tinworth with monogram.

28   Joseph telling Jacob about the sons of Bilhah and Zilpah. 26 × 23·5 cm. Glass broken.

28   The angels bringing Lot and his wife and daughters out of Sodom and Gomorrah: Psalm 37 35 Vers: All flesh is grass and all the goodliness thereof as the flowers of the field: Take heed unto thyself be sober and watch to the end. H Doulton & Co Lambeth. 29 × 14 cm.

28   The four lepers outside Samaria: Second Book of Kings VII Chapt: Psalm CVII: Our poverty in the Lords hands is often the meanes of bringing plenty to our poor: He that witholdeth corn the people shall curse him. 31 × 14 cm.

28   And when the child was grown, it fell on a day, that he went out to his father to the reapers, and he said unto his father my head my head: Shall we receive good at the hand of God, and shall we not receive evil? 31 × 13·5 cm.

29   The man and the seven sons of Sceva: How shall they preach except they be sent: Acts XIX Chapt 13 Ver: Is your eye concentrated this time upon the principal figure. 19 × 17 cm.

29   The death of Eli: Whether we live or whether we die we are the Lords: He fell from off the seat backward. 18 × 17 cm.

29   The unjust judge parable: Hold fast till I come: If any man draw back my soul shall have no pleasure in him (On the door of the room depicted is 'Mr Graball no money no hope') 19·5 × 18·5 cm.

29   Then Herod when he saw that he was mocked of the Wise Men, was exceeding wroth and sent forth and slew all the children that was in Bethlehem: Better is a wise child than an old and foolish King who will be no more admonished. 31 × 14 cm.

29   The judgement of Solomon: And she said O my Lord give her the living child and in no wise slay it but the other said let it be neither mine nor thine but divide it: It is the glory of God to conceal a thing but the honour of kings is to search out a matter. 31 × 14 cm.

30   Finding the body of the man of God: The man is taken and the donkeys left: It often happens so perils among false bretheren: I of Kings XIII. 17 × 17 cm.

30   Joseph in the pit: Before honor is humility: A wounded spirit who can bear: Pro XX 22 V. 27 × 16 cm.

30   The Lord's Supper. Moulded low relief. 21 × 21 cm.

30   The Philistines surprising Samson: Delilah the woman that would sell you. Moulded low relief. 38 × 21 cm.

30   The Death of Jacob. 39 × 26 cm.

7/11 Puzzle jug. Unmarked. See p.11

9/10 Jug by R. W. Martin, 1874. See p.12

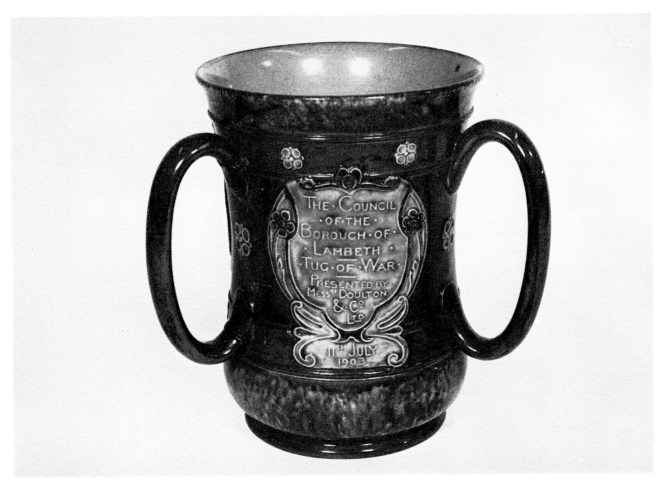

4/4 Loving cup. Doulton. See p.10

16/2 Bowl with relief panels. Doulton. See p.14

18

4/1 Loving cup by Hannah B. Barlow. Doulton. See p.10

4/7 Loving cup with horse-racing scenes. Doulton. See p.10

7/9 Toby Filpot jug. Unmarked. See p.11

14/6 Flask, marked 'Smith Lambeth'. See p.13

14/11 Old woman flask. Unmarked. See p.13

7/12 Head of Duke of Wellington jug. Marked 'Stephen Green, Lambeth'. See p.11

2/3 Mug in agate fabric, Doulton. See p.9

10/8 Jug, probably made in Scotland. See p.12

7/10 Monkey coffee-pot, shown with lid raised. Unmarked. See p.11

16/15 Vase by Louisa E. Edwards. Doulton. See p.14

16/13 Vase by Arthur B. Barlow. Doulton. See p.14

18/1 'Character' head bottle. Unmarked. See p.13

2/4 Queen Victoria jubilee mug, Doulton. See p.9.   3/10 National Rifle Association beaker, Doulton. See p.9

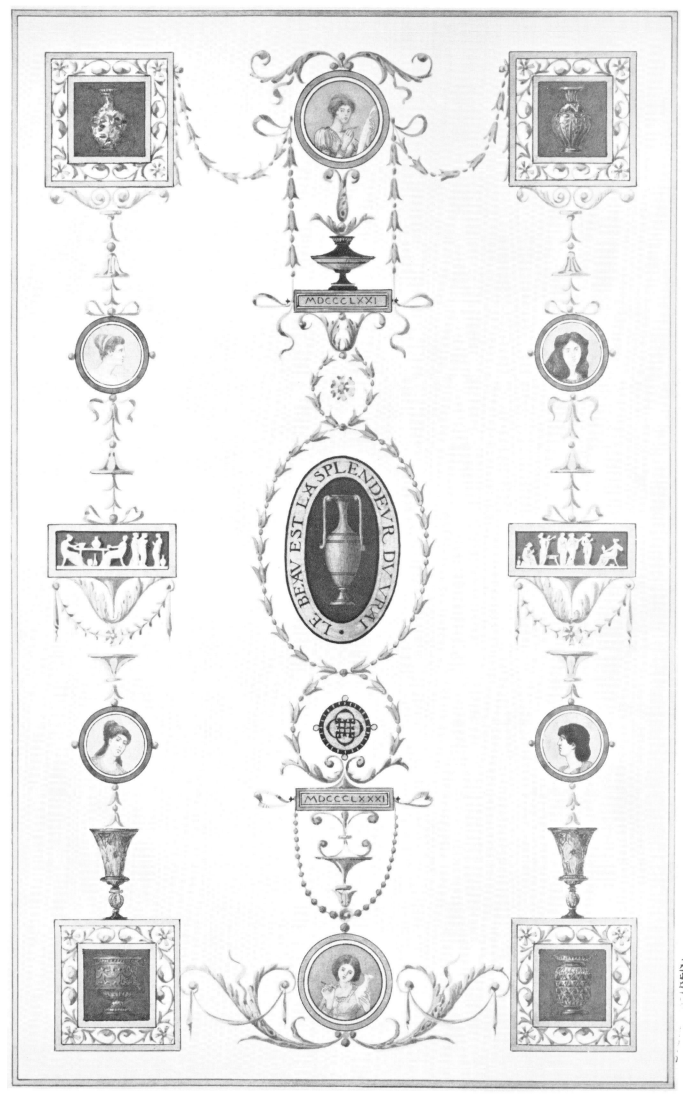

LE BEAV EST LA SPLENDEVR DV VRAI

MDCCCLXXI

MDCCCLXXXI

ALBERT EMBANKMENT BUILDINGS

DESIGN IN BEAVTY   BVILD IN TRVTH

TO HENRY DOVLTON ESQre

CHEVALIER OF THE LEGION OF HONOR.

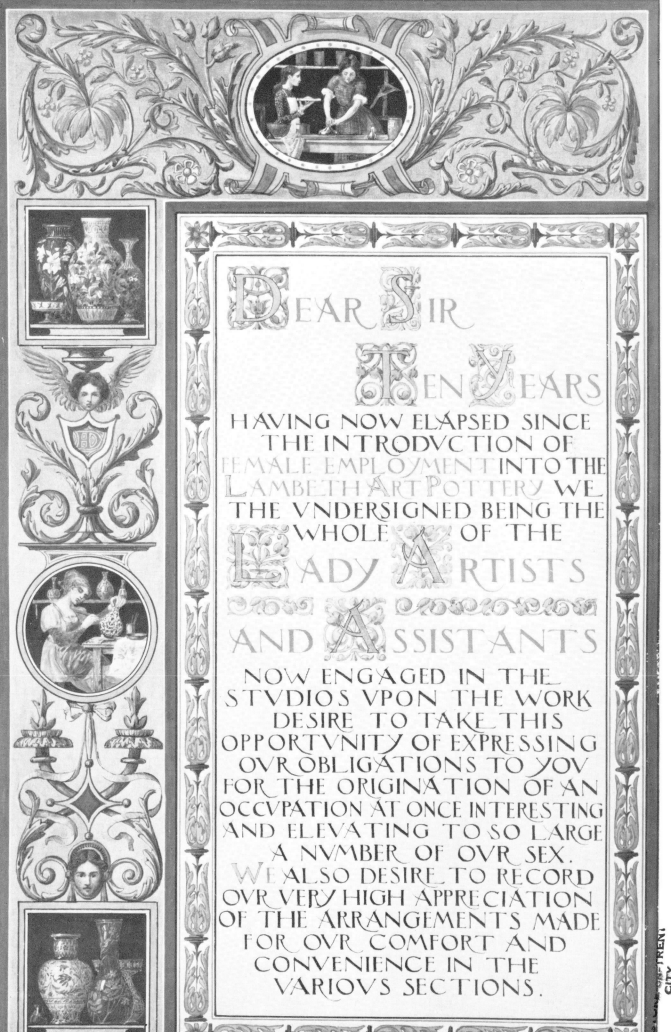

Dear Sir

Ten Years

HAVING NOW ELAPSED SINCE
THE INTRODVCTION OF
FEMALE EMPLOYMENT INTO THE
LAMBETH ART POTTERY WE
THE VNDERSIGNED BEING THE
WHOLE OF THE

Lady Artists

AND Assistants

NOW ENGAGED IN THE
STVDIOS VPON THE WORK
DESIRE TO TAKE THIS
OPPORTVNITY OF EXPRESSING
OVR OBLIGATIONS TO YOV
FOR THE ORIGINATION OF AN
OCCVPATION AT ONCE INTERESTING
AND ELEVATING TO SO LARGE
A NVMBER OF OVR SEX.
WE ALSO DESIRE TO RECORD
OVR VERY HIGH APPRECIATION
OF THE ARRANGEMENTS MADE
FOR OVR COMFORT AND
CONVENIENCE IN THE
VARIOVS SECTIONS.

EACH YEAR SINCE THE OPENING
OF THE ART STVDIOS HAS SEEN
A LARGE INCREASE IN OVR
NVMBERS AND AN EXTENSION
OF THE VARIETY OF DECORATION
THERE HAS ALSO BEEN AN
EXTENDED PATRONAGE AND
APPRECIATION ON THE PART
OF ART CRITICS AND THE
PVBLIC, WHILE THE CONTINVED
DEMAND FOR OVR PRODVCTIONS
LEADS VS TO THE CONVICTION
THAT WE ARE FVLLY JVSTIFIED
IN CONGRATVLATING YOV
ON THE MARKED SVCCESS OF
THE VNDERTAKING.
WE WOVLD EXPRESS OVR HOPE
THAT THE DEPARTMENT WHICH
HAS SO AVSPICIOVSLY
COMPLETED ITS FIRST DECENNIVM
MAY LONG CONTINVE TO
PROSPER AND ASSVRE YOV TO
THIS END NO EFFORT ON OVR
PART SHALL BE WANTING.
WISHING YOV CONTINVED
HEALTH AND PROSPERITY,
WE ARE DEAR SIR
WITH MVCH RESPECT
YOVRS MOST FAITHFVLLY,

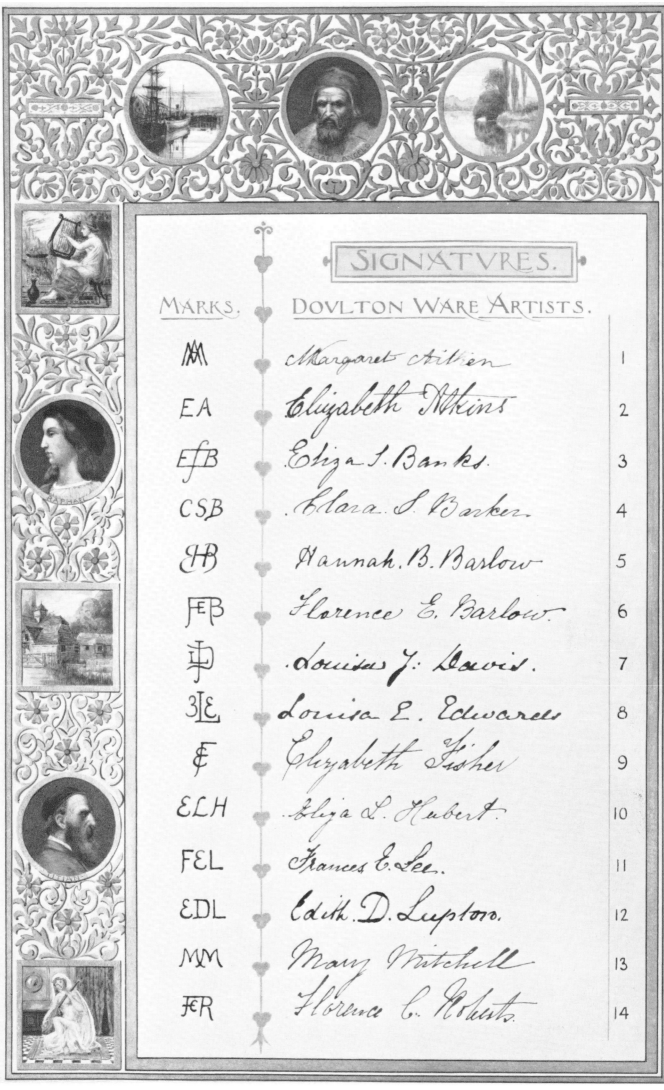

SIGNATVRES.

MARKS.	DOVLTON WARE ARTISTS.	
ᛗ	Margaret Aitken	1
EA	Elizabeth Atkins	2
EℓB	Eliza S. Banks.	3
CSB	Clara S. Barker	4
HB	Hannah. B. Barlow	5
FEB	Florence E. Barlow.	6
⅁	Louisa J. Davis.	7
3E	Louisa E. Edwards.	8
ℰ	Elizabeth Fisher	9
ELH	Eliza L. Hubert.	10
FEL	Frances E. Lee.	11
EDL	Edith D. Lupton.	12
MM	Mary Mitchell	13
FCR	Florence C. Roberts.	14

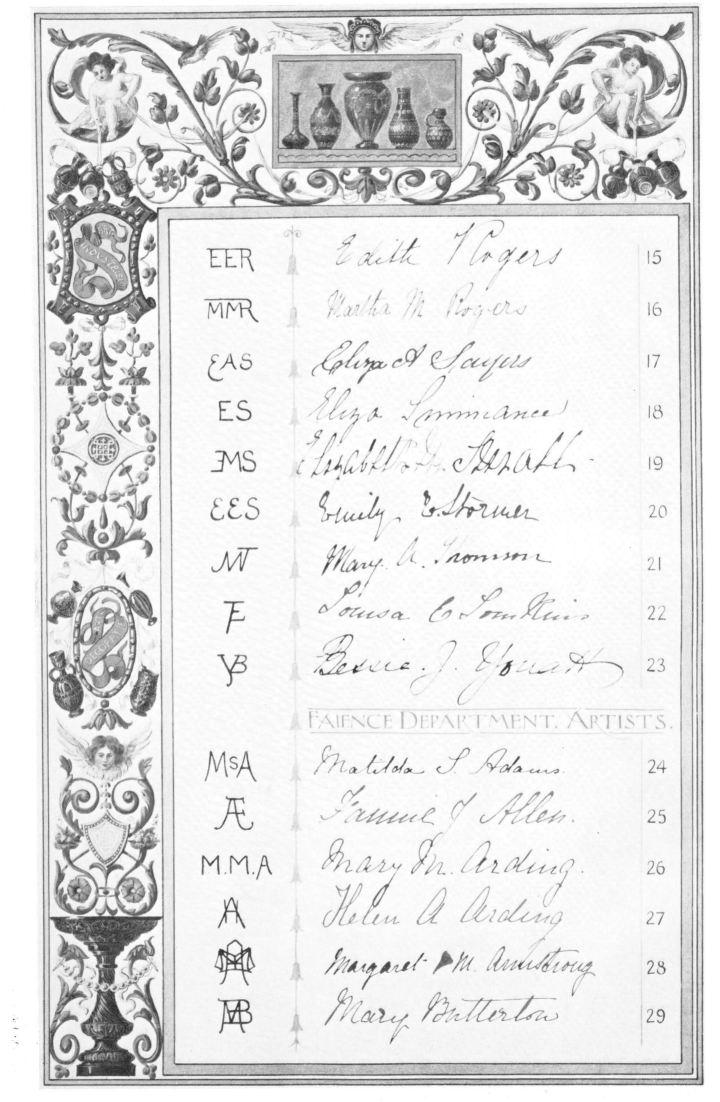

EER	Edith Rogers	15
MMR	Martha M. Rogers	16
EAS	Eliza A Sayers	17
ES	Eliza Simmance	18
EMS	Elizabeth M. Small	19
EES	Emily E. Stormer	20
MT	Mary A. Thomson	21
F	Louisa C Tomkins	22
YB	Bessie J. Youatt	23

FAIENCE DEPARTMENT. ARTISTS.

MsA	Matilda S. Adams	24
Æ	Fannie J Allen	25
M.M.A	Mary M. Arding	26
A	Helen A Arding	27
MA	Margaret M. Armstrong	28
MB	Mary Butterton	29

M C	Mary Capes.	30
M C	Margaret Challis	31
M C	Minna Cranley.	32
F E	F Elliott	33
A G	Alberta L. Green	34
✠ A	Alice Hall.	35
H L	Lizzie Haughton.	36
R K	Rosa Keen.	37
U L	Ubrigne Larcher	38
E.H.	Elizabeth Hamilton	39
E L	Esther Lewis	40
F L	Florence Lewis	41
I L	Isabel Lewis	42
F L	Frances M. Linnell.	43
E R	Emmie Roberts	44
K R	Kate Rogers	45
F.S.	Fanny Stable	46

$		Katie Sturgeon.	47
Æ		A E Thatcher	48
W Latt		Linnie Watt	49

DOVLTON WARE, SENIOR ASSISTANTS.

MA		Mary Aitken	50
a ▪▪		Lizzie Axford.	51
a		Louisa Ayling	52
B̄	bᵠ	Edith H. Ball	53
B̲	b▪	Alice M. E. Barker	54
B.		Jessie Bowditch	55
bb▪		Eliza Bowen	56
R.B.		Rosina Brown	57
b+		Georgina Burr	58
AEB. b		Alice E. Budden	59
ALB. B		Alice L. Burlton.	60
ⓑ		Eleanor Burrell	61

O b	Emma A Burrows	62
c	Kate J Castle	63
I C	Emily M. Chandler.	64
FC	Fanny Clark	65
E.C.	Edith M Coleman	66
cOO	Emily Crosby	67
cc	Annie Cupit.	68
C c■	S A Lilian Curtis.	69
dO	Lizzie Marie Daintree	70
K.D.	Kate M. Davis	71
MD d+	Mary A Davis	72
AD d■	Ada Dennis.	73
dd	S. Imogen Durtnall.	74
e■■	Florence Earl	75
e■	Alice Eckenstein.	76
eeO	Lottie Eckenstein	77

Ǝ e	Bertha Evans	78
e e	Kate Everett	79
SF ⓕ	Sarah Fisher	80
f O	Emily A Forsey	81
ff	Lizzie French	82
EG g	Nellie Garbott	83
ⓖ	Sarah P. Gathercole	84
NG g g ▬	Ellen Gathercole	85
A.G.	Annie Gentle	86
G. g O	Kate R. Giblin	87
g g	Mary A. Goode	88
.G.	Alice Green	89
g ▬	Laura Green	90
R.H.	Rosina Harris	91
hh ▬	Emily Hawksby	92
H h ▬	Alice M. Heapath	93

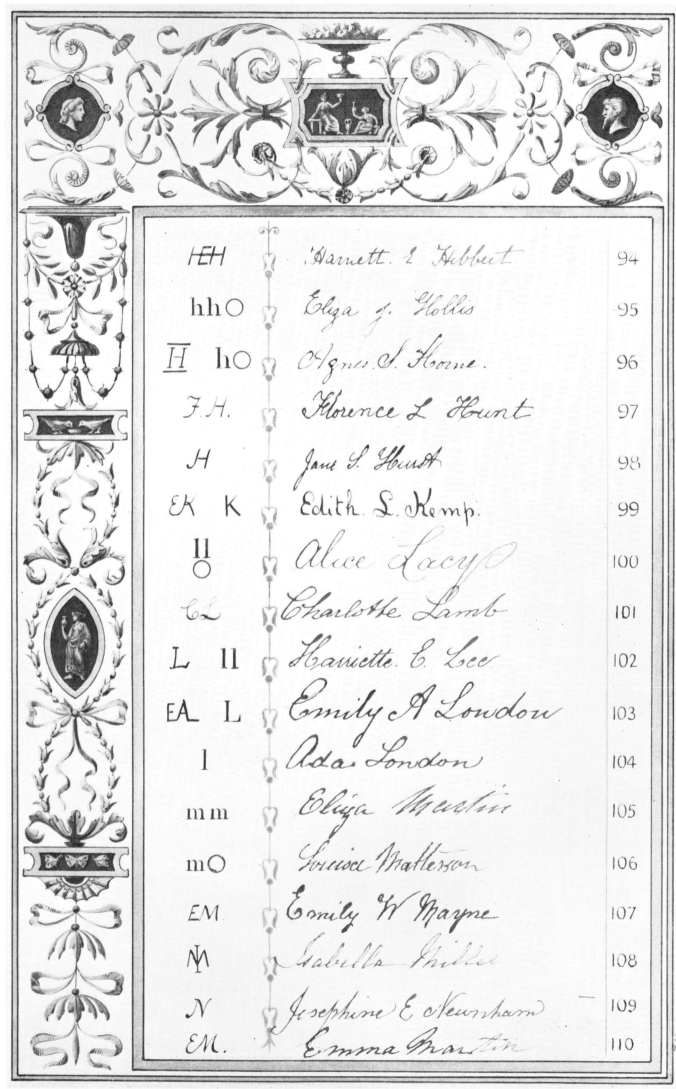

HEH	Harriett E Hibbert	94
hhO	Eliza J. Hollis	95
H̲ hO	Agnes S. Horne.	96
F.H.	Florence L. Hunt	97
JH	Jane S. Hurst	98
EK K	Edith L. Kemp.	99
llO	Alice Lacy	100
CL	Charlotte Lamb	101
L ll	Harriette E. Lee	102
EA L	Emily A London	103
l	Ada London	104
mm	Eliza Martin	105
mO	Louisa Matterson	106
EM.	Emily W Mayne	107
NM	Isabella Mills	108
N	Josephine E Newnham	109
EM.	Emma Martin	110

p	Lizzie Padbury	111
EP	Emily J. Partington	112
rrO	Jane Rabbet	113
R r:	Constance E. Redford	114
AR	Alice M. Ritchin.	115
(r)	Alice Robjent	116
r	Letitia Rosevear	117
ER RO	Ellen Rumbol	118
AS. sO	A Sayers	119
ES.	Emma Shute	120
S. ss	Ellen B Smith	121
SMS s:	Mary Storey	122
MGT	Minnie Thompson.	123
v	Bessie M. Varney	124
LW w	Louisa Wakely	125
EW	Emily M. R. Welch.	126

FAIENCE DEPARTMENT, SENIOR ASSISTANTS.

Monogram	Name	Page
BC	Bertha M Capes.	127
E	Ellen Crosby	128
D	Beatrice M. Durtnall.	129
A.D.	Amelia A Drake.	130
AF	Ada E Finister.	131
H	Emma C. Harrison	132
H.x.	Annie M Hulford	133
EM	Iza. M. Munday.	134
N	Lilla Nottingham	135
R	Emily L Robinson	136
AR	Agnes. M. Ruff.	137
S.S	Susanna M. Sanderson	138
E.S	Elizabeth Shelley.	139
SL	Lizzie Shettleworth.	140
M.S.	Mary L Slatter	141

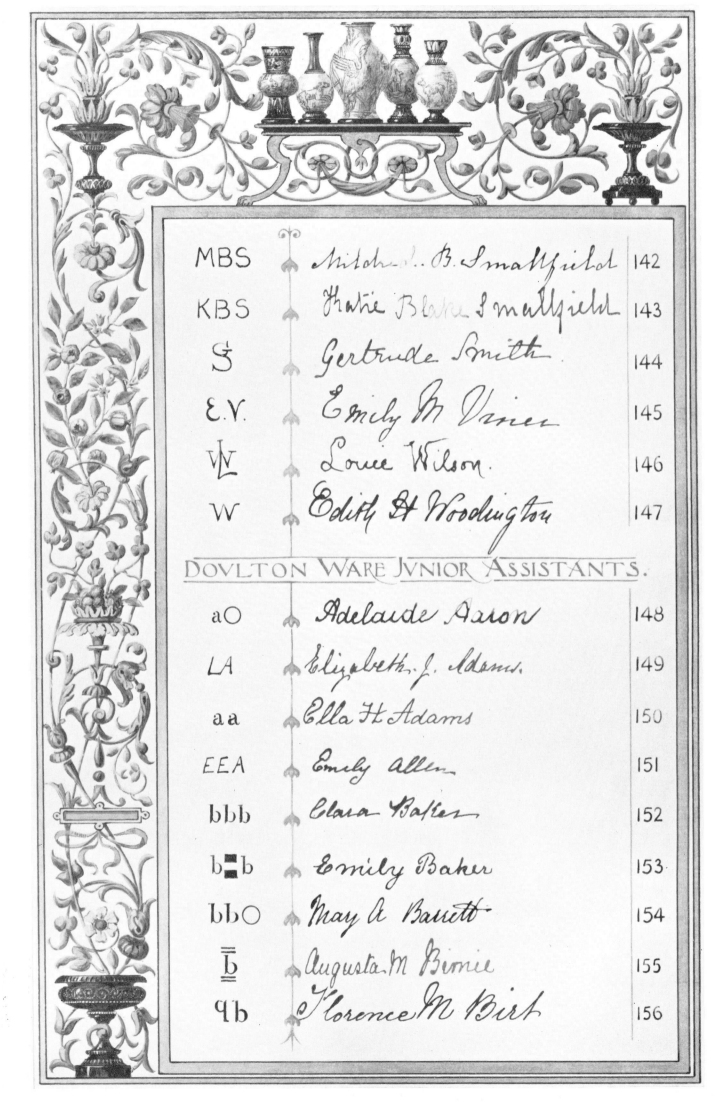

MBS		Mitchell B. Smallfield	142
KBS		Katie Blake Smallfield	143
G̶S		Gertrude Smith	144
E.V.		Emily M Viner	145
WL		Louie Wilson	146
W		Edith H Woodington	147

DOVLTON WARE JVNIOR ASSISTANTS.

aO		Adelaide Aaron	148
LA		Elizabeth J. Adams	149
a a		Ella H Adams	150
EEA		Emily Allen	151
bbb		Clara Baker	152
b▪▪b		Emily Baker	153
bbO		May A Barrett	154
b̿		Augusta M Birnie	155
ꝗb		Florence M Birt	156

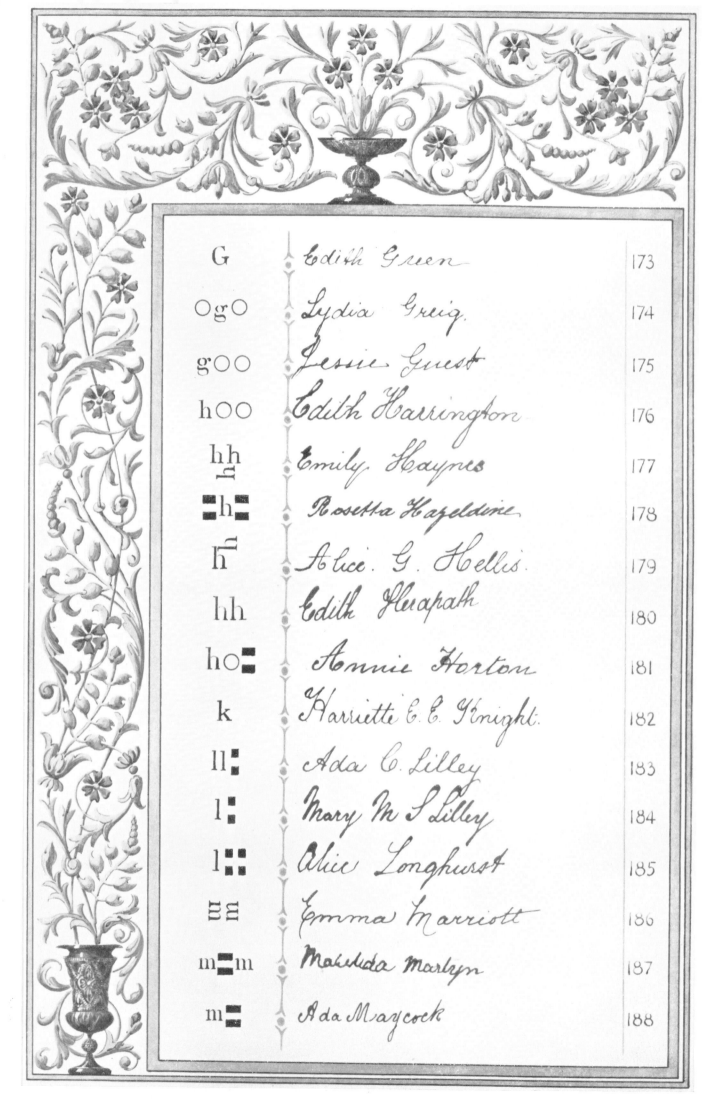

G	Edith Green	173
OgO	Lydia Greig	174
gOO	Jessie Guest	175
hOO	Edith Harrington	176
hh	Emily Haynes	177
h	Rosetta Hazeldine	178
h	Alice G. Hellis	179
hh	Edith Heapath	180
hO	Annie Horton	181
k	Harriette E. E. Knight	182
ll	Ada C. Lilley	183
l	Mary M S Lilley	184
l	Alice Longhurst	185
m	Emma Marriott	186
m m	Matilda Martyn	187
m	Ada Maycock	188

m	Emily Mayes.	189
▄▄ m	Alice Wilbonow	190
ⓜ	Annie Milne.	191
m ○○	Ada Morgan	192
n	Annie Neal	193
○ p	Ellen Palmer.	194
p ▄	Annie Partridge	195
P ▄ P	Georgina Pearson	196
pp	Helena M. Pennett	197
E.R.	Emily Randall.	198
r ○○	Jane Rumbol	199
▄ r ▄	Alice Russell	200
R ▄ᵣ▄	Louisa Russell.	201
r ɹ	Kate E. Russell	202
r ○	Clara Rymer.	203
s ○○	Fanny Sayers	204

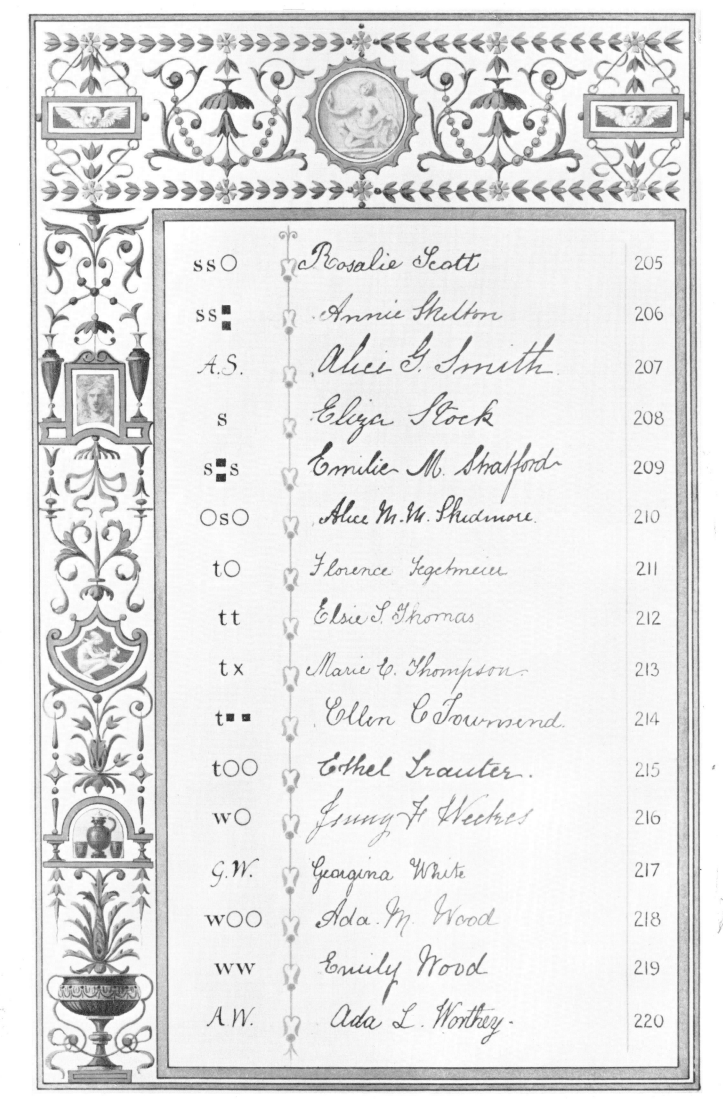

ssO	Rosalie Scott	205
ss∎	Annie Skelton	206
A.S.	Alice G. Smith	207
s	Eliza Stock	208
s∎s	Emilie M. Stratford	209
OsO	Alice M. M. Skidmore	210
tO	Florence Tegetmeier	211
tt	Elsie S. Thomas	212
tx	Marie C. Thompson	213
t∎∎	Ellen C Townsend	214
tOO	Ethel Trauter	215
wO	Jenny F. Weekes	216
G.W.	Georgina White	217
wOO	Ada M. Wood	218
ww	Emily Wood	219
A.W.	Ada L. Worthey	220

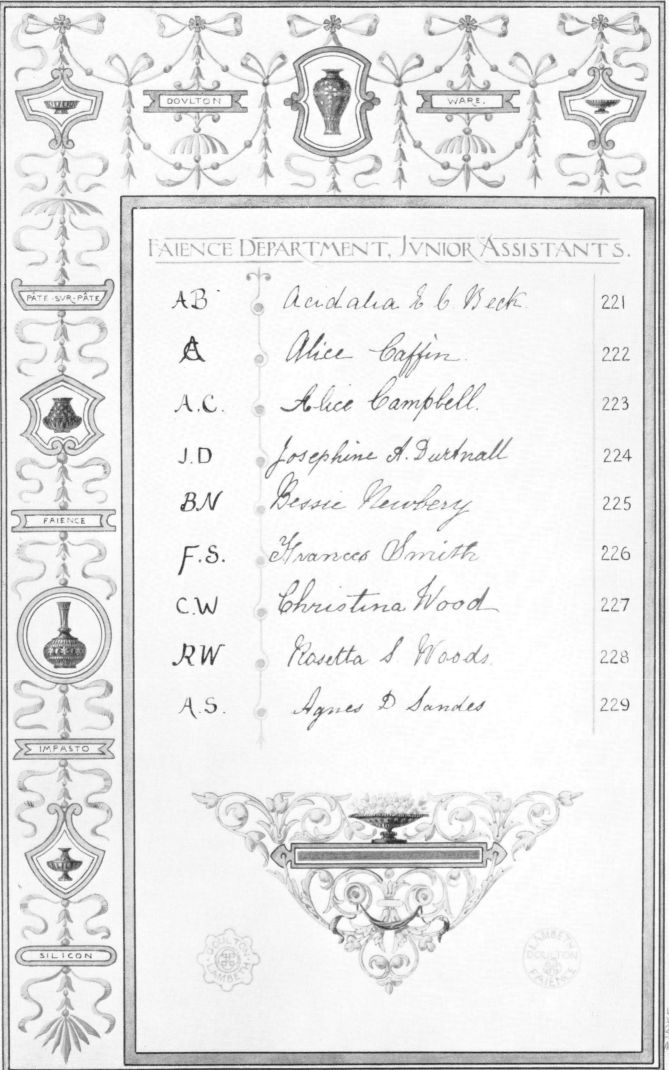

FAIENCE DEPARTMENT, JUNIOR ASSISTANTS.

Mark	Name	Page
AB	Acidalia E C Beck	221
A	Alice Caffin	222
A.C.	Alice Campbell	223
J.D	Josephine A. Durtnall	224
BN	Bessie Newbery	225
F.S.	Frances Smith	226
C.W	Christina Wood	227
RW	Rosetta S Woods	228
A.S.	Agnes D Sandes	229

APPENDIX Nº 1

LIST OF ARTISTS NOW CONNECTED WITH LAMBETH ART POTTERY NOT INCLUDED IN THE SIGNATURES

MARK	NAME
	GEORGE. TINWORTH.
	JOHN. BROAD.
	HERBERT. ELLIS.
	JOHN. HUSKINSON.
M.V.M.	MARK. V. MARSHALL.
	WILLIAM. PARKER.
	HARRY. BARNARD.
	GEORGE. H. TABOR.
	FRANK. A. BUTLER.
	GEORGE. W. RHEAD.
J.H.M.	JOHN. H. McLENNAN.
	JAMES. R. CRUICKSHANK.
	ARTHUR. E. PEARCE.

LIST OF ASSISTANTS NOT INCLUDED IN THE SIGNATURES

MARK	NAME
	FRANK. W. READER.
	EDGAR. W. WILSON.
.P.	FRANK. POPE.
	GEORGE. W. BEARNE.
	ERNEST. R. BISHOP.
	ARTHUR. WILCOCK.
	WALTER. THORNEMAN.

APPENDIX Nº 2

SHOWING YEARLY INCREASE IN NVMBER OF LADY ARTISTS AND ASSISTANTS EMPLOYED IN LAMBETH ART POTTERY.

JVNE	1871.	Nº 1.
JVNE	1872.	Nº 1.
FEBRVARY	1873.	Nº 6.
DECEMBER	1873.	Nº 13.
DECEMBER	1874.	Nº 30.
DECEMBER	1875.	Nº 44.
DECEMBER	1876.	Nº 74.
DECEMBER	1877.	Nº 92.
DECEMBER	1878.	Nº 113.
DECEMBER	1879.	Nº 148.
DECEMBER	1880.	Nº 171.
DECEMBER	1881.	Nº 231.

APPENDIX Nº 3

LIST OF AWARDS OBTAINED FOR
LAMBETH ART POTTERY.

1871. SOUTH KENSINGTON. ANNUAL INTERNATIONAL EXHIBITION.
HONORABLE MENTION.

1871. PERU. INTERNATIONAL EXHIBITION.
FIRST CLASS AWARD.

1872. SOUTH KENSINGTON. ANNUAL INTERNATIONAL EXHIBITION.
HONORABLE MENTION.

1872. DUBLIN. EXHIBITION.
SILVER MEDAL.

1872. LYONS. INTERNATIONAL EXHIBITION.
SILVER MEDAL.

1873. VIENNA. INTERNATIONAL EXHIBITION.
FIRST CLASS MEDAL FOR PROGRESS.

1873. VERSAILLES. CONCOURS REGIONAL.
GOLD MEDAL.

1875. CHILI. INTERNATIONAL EXHIBITION.
SECOND PRIZE.

1876. PHILADELPHIA. INTERNATIONAL EXHIBITION.
FIRST CLASS AWARD.

1877. CAPE OF GOOD HOPE. INTERNATIONAL EXHIBITION.
GOLD MEDAL.

1878. PARIS. INTERNATIONAL EXHIBITION.
GRAND PRIX.

1879. PARIS. INTERNATIONAL EXHIBITION OF ARTS
AND SCIENCES APPLIED TO INDUSTRY. DIPLOMA OF HONOR.

1879. SIDNEY. INTERNATIONAL EXHIBITION.
ONLY FIRST CLASS AWARD.

1879. YORK. FINE ART EXHIBITION.
FIRST CLASS MEDAL (BRONZE.)

1880. MELBOURNE. INTERNATIONAL EXHIBITION.
GOLD MEDAL.

1881. SOUTH KENSINGTON. PARKES MUSEUM OF HYGIENE.
FIRST CLASS CERTIFICATE.

1881. EASTBOURNE. EXHIBITION OF FINE ART AND
SANITARY APPLIANCES. SILVER MEDAL.

1881. BRIGHTON. EXHIBITION OF FINE ART & C.
ONLY GOLD MEDAL.

APPENDIX Nº 4

LIST OF DISTINGVISHED PERSONS WHO HAVE VISITED THE STVDIOS AND SHOW ROOMS.

H.R.H. THE PRINCESS OF WALES.

H.R.H. THE DVKE OF CONNAVGHT, K.G., K.T., K.P., G.S.C.I.

H.R.H. THE CROWN PRINCESS OF PRVSSIA.

H.R.H. THE CROWN PRINCE OF PRVSSIA, K.G.

H.R.H. THE COVNT OF FLANDERS.

H.R.H. THE COVNTESS OF FLANDERS.

THE PRINCESS VICTORIA.   CHILDREN OF

THE PRINCE ADOLPHVS. } H.R.H. THE DVTCHESS OF TECK.

THE PRINCE FRANCIS.

THE SIAMESE AMBASSADOR AND SVITE.

HIS GRACE THE ARCHBISHOP OF CANTERBVRY, P.C., F.R.S.

HIS GRACE THE DVKE OF SVTHERLAND, K.G.

HIS GRACE THE DVKE OF HAMILTON. K.T.

THE MARQVIS OF NORTHAMPTON.

THE EARL OF DENBIGH.

EARL FORTESCVE, F.S.S.

EARL BROWNLOW.

EARL CATHCART.

THE DOWAGER COVNTESS OF MAR AND KELLIE.

VISCOVNT CRANBROOK, P.C., G.C.S.I.

THE Rᵀ HON. W.E.GLADSTONE, M.P., D.C.L., F.S.S.

THE Rᵀ HON. JOHN BRIGHT, M.P.

THE Rᵀ HON. SIR STAFFORD H.NORTHCOTE. BARᵀ,
M.P., G.C.B, D.C.L.

LORD RONALD SUTHERLAND GOWER.

THE REVᴰ LORD ALWYNE COMPTON, M.A.

LADY ALWYNE COMPTON.

LORD MONTEAGLE.

LADY PAGET.

LADY MARIAN ALFORD.

LIEVT. GENˡ SIR GARNET J. WOLSELEY, G.C.M.G, G.C.B.

SIR PHILIP CUNLIFFE OWEN, K.C.M.G, C.B, C.I.E.

SIR RUTHERFORD ALCOCK, K.C.B, F.R.G.S.

SIR THEOPHILUS SHEPSTONE.

SIR G.C.M. BIRDWOOD, C.S.I.

THE HON DUDLEY FRAˢ FORTESCUE, F.R.G.S, F.G.S.

THE VERY REVᴰ DEAN OF YORK,

THE VERY REVᴰ Dᴿ CHURCH, DEAN OF Sᵀ PAULS.

CANON FARRAR, D.D.

CANON GREGORY, M.A.

G.E. STREET ESQᴿᴱ, R.A.

G.F. WATTS ESQᴿᴱ, R.A.

E.J. POYNTER ESQᴿᴱ, R.A.

H.S. MARKS ESQᴿᴱ, R.A.

M. GUSTAVE DORÉ.

HARRISON WEIR ESQᴿᴱ

G.H. LEWES ESQᴿᴱ AND Mᴿˢ LEWES. (GEORGE ELIOT.)

JOHN RUSKIN ESQᴿᴱ

TOM TAYLOR ESQᴿᴱ

SPECIMENS OF THE LAMBETH ART POTTERY WERE
SUBMITTED FOR INSPECTION, BY COMMAND OF
HER MAJESTY THE QUEEN, AT WINDSOR CASTLE.